WHICH IS WORSE?

2

By Lee Taylor

CRAZY QUESTIONS TO ASK YOUR FRIENDS!

SCHOLASTIC INC.

ISBN 978-1-338-26432-6

10 9 8 7 6 5 4 3 2 1   18 19 20 21 22

Printed in the U.S.A.   40
First edition, September 2018

Book design by Kay Petronio

How do you choose between
bad and worse?!
It's time to find out. Snag your friends,
grab a snack, and hunker down for more than
100 crazy new questions that **MAKE** you choose.
Some are embarrassing, some are scary,
and some are totally gross.

But **NONE** of them are good.

So go ahead and choose . . .

WHICH ‹IS› WORSE???

WHICH IS WORSE

YOUR SNACK GETTING STUCK IN THE VENDING MACHINE

THE BLOOD IN YOUR VEINS

freezing

OR

boiling?

???

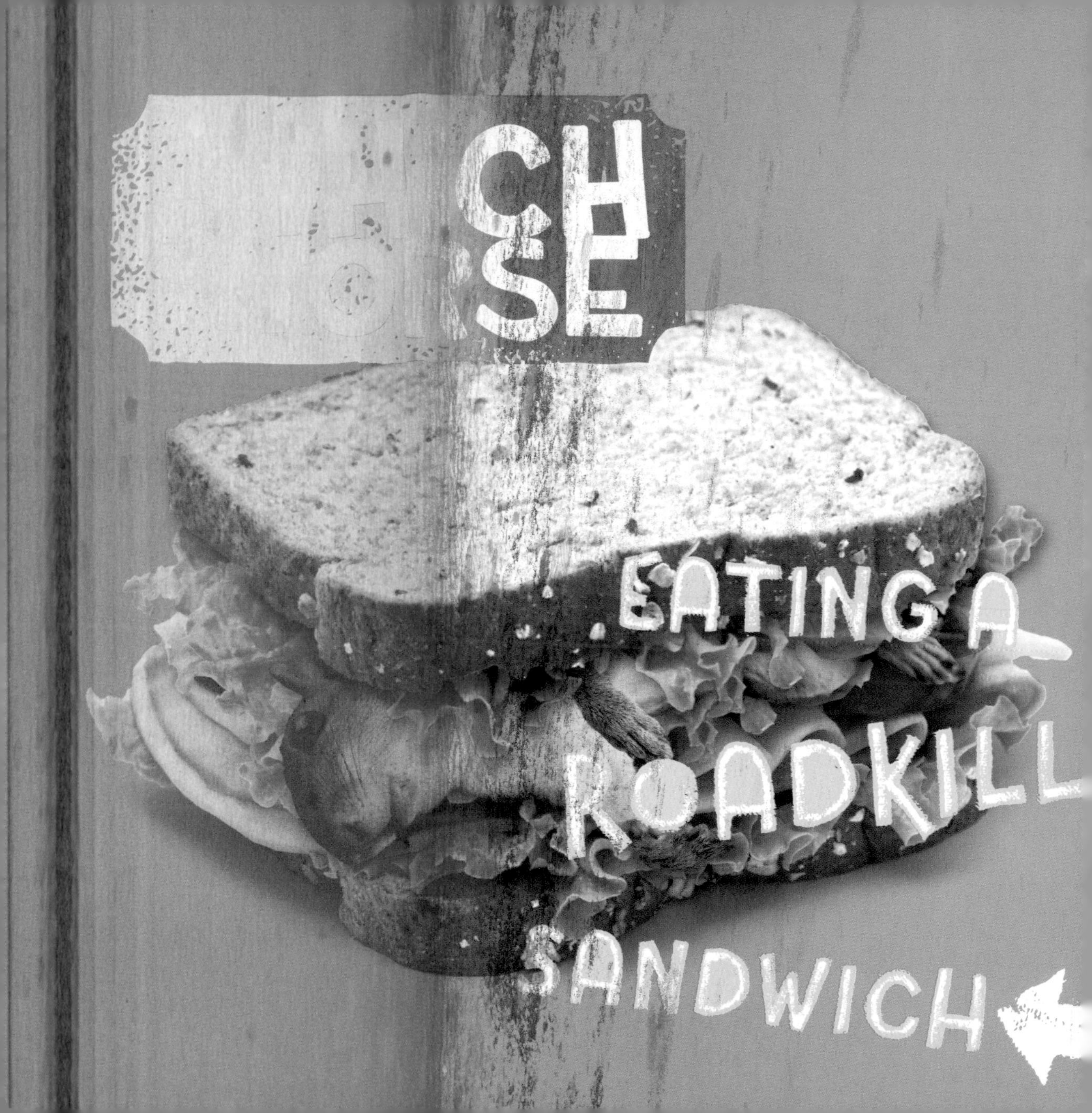
CH
SE
EATING A
ROADKILL
SANDWICH

OR

ROTTEN-FISH SOUP?

WHICH IS WORSE

BEING STUCK IN A DIRTY DIAPER

◄OR►

A STRAITJACKET?

WHICH IS WORSE

HAVING acne FOR LIFE

OR

A BO PROBLEM FOR LIFE?

USING **HOT SAUCE** AS EYE DROPS

OR

GHOST PEPPERS AS SOAP?

WHICH IS WORSE

getting caught in the GREAT CHICAGO FIRE

OR

the GREAT SAN FRANCISCO EARTHQUAKE?

WHICH IS WORSE

being stuck in a **BROKEN** elevator overnight

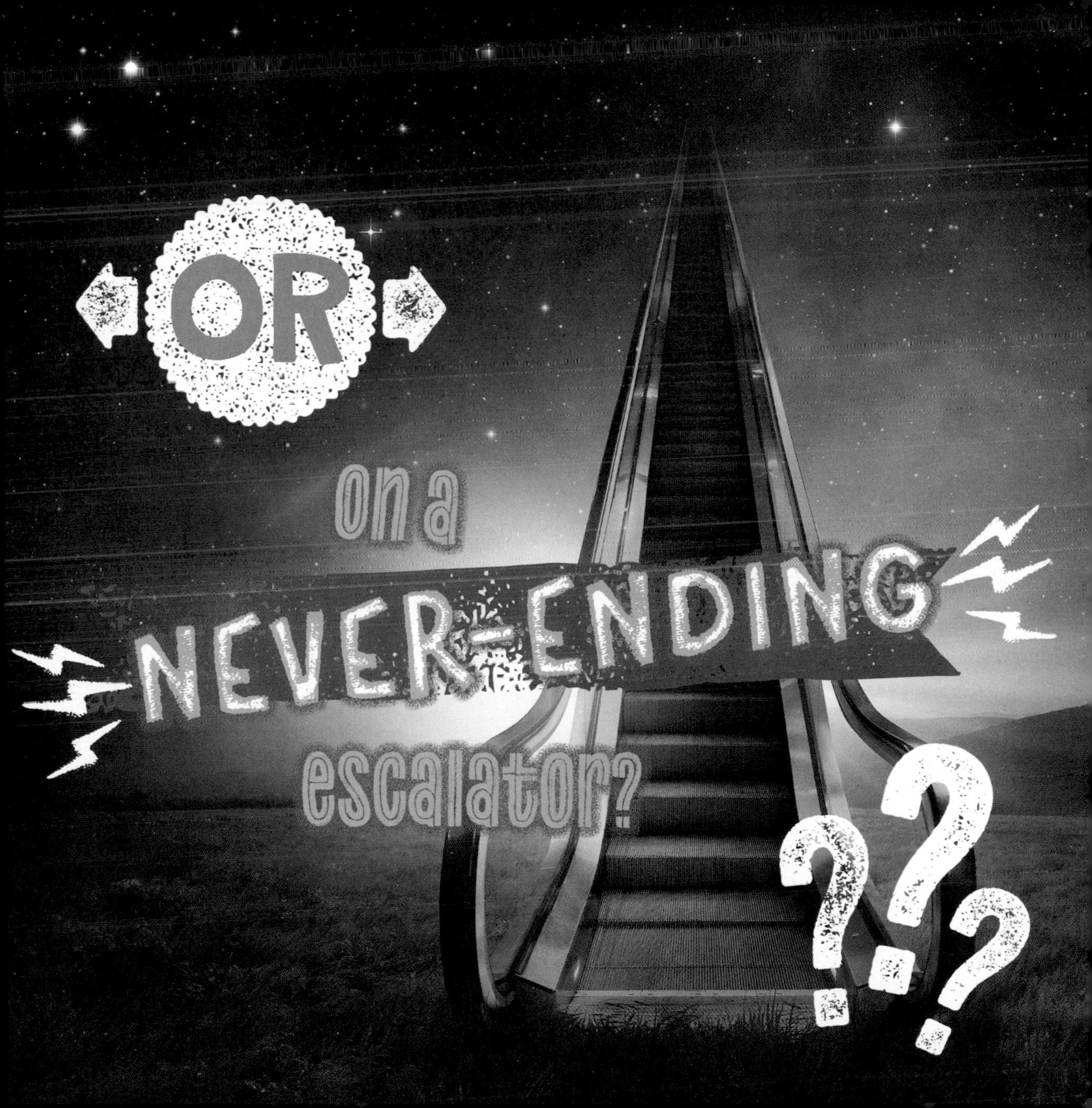
OR
on a
NEVER-ENDING
escalator?

WHICH IS WORSE

TALKING TO SOMEONE WHEN YOU HAVE REALLY BAD BREATH

OR

SOMETHING
STUCK
IN YOUR
TEETH?

? ? ?

WHICH IS WORSE

your best friend **cropping you out** of their profile pic

OR

secretly getting

unfriended
by everyone

you know?

???

WHICH IS WORSE

(IS

WORSE

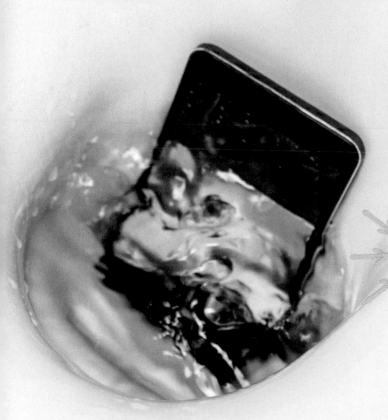

DROPPING YOUR **PHONE** IN THE **TOILET**

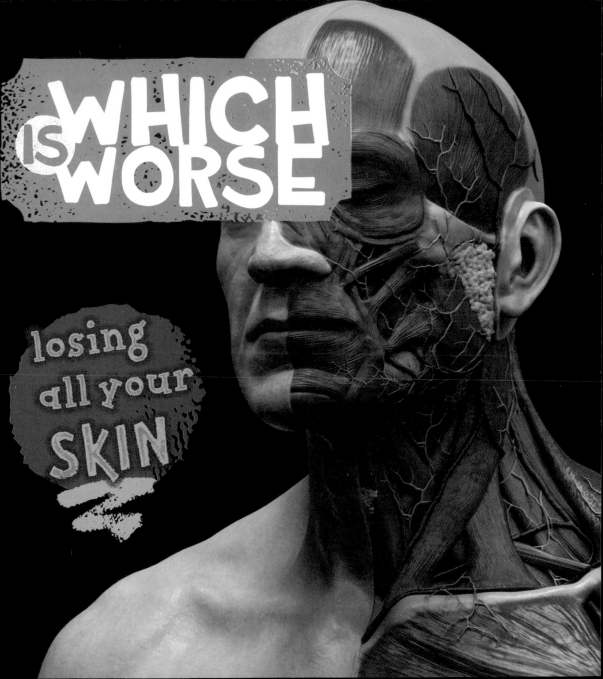

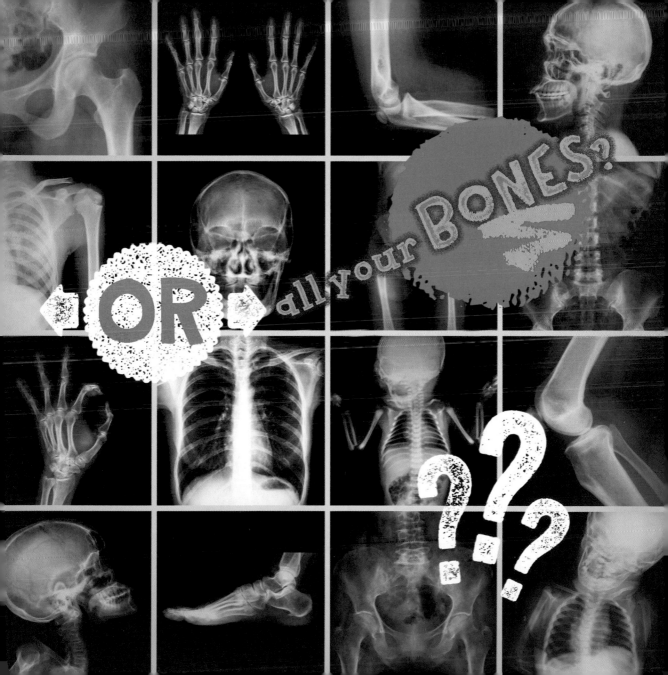

OR all your BONES?

WHICH IS WORSE

WAITING IN LINE FOR **HOURS** TO RIDE A *roller coaster*

OR GETTING ON **IMMEDIATELY** ONLY TO HAVE IT *break down?*

WHICH IS WORSE

WEARING clothes MADE OF algae

WHICH IS WORSE

GETTING ATTACKED BY A MAD SCIENTIST

OR A LIVING MUMMY?

TOPPING **YOUR** SUNDAE WITH

earwax

OR

TOPPING IT WITH

dandruff?

WHICH IS WORSE

GETTING TURNED INTO A ZOMBIE

OR EATEN BY ONE?

????

WHICH IS WORSE

CAMPING IN THE SAHARA

OR

CAMPING IN SIBERIA?

???

WHICH IS WORSE

BECOMING A PROFESSIONAL ATHLETE WHO NEVER PLAYS

WHICH IS WORSE

ONLY BEING ABLE TO whisper

WHICH IS WORSE

LIVING WITH NO **ELECTRICITY**

WHICH IS WORSE

C www.googie.com

+You   Search   Images   Maps   Mail   More

EVERYONE SEEING YOUR INTERNET SEARCH HISTORY

Goog

WHICH IS WORSE

WEARING A COAT IN Death Valley

WHICH IS WORSE

HAVING A → TAPEWORM IN YOUR INTESTINES ←

OR

A TICK ON YOUR SCALP?

???

WHICH IS WORSE

NEEDING TO YAWN EVERY *few* seconds

OR

SNEEZE EVERY *few seconds?*

WHICH IS WORSE

HAVING A NEVER-ENDING **headache**

OR

BEING CONSTANTLY **dizzy?**

BEING ABLE TO **SHAPESHIFT** — BUT ONLY INTO OFFICE SUPPLIES

OR

BEING ABLE TO **STOP TIME** — BUT ONLY FOR A SECOND?

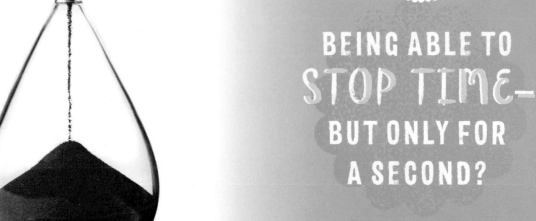

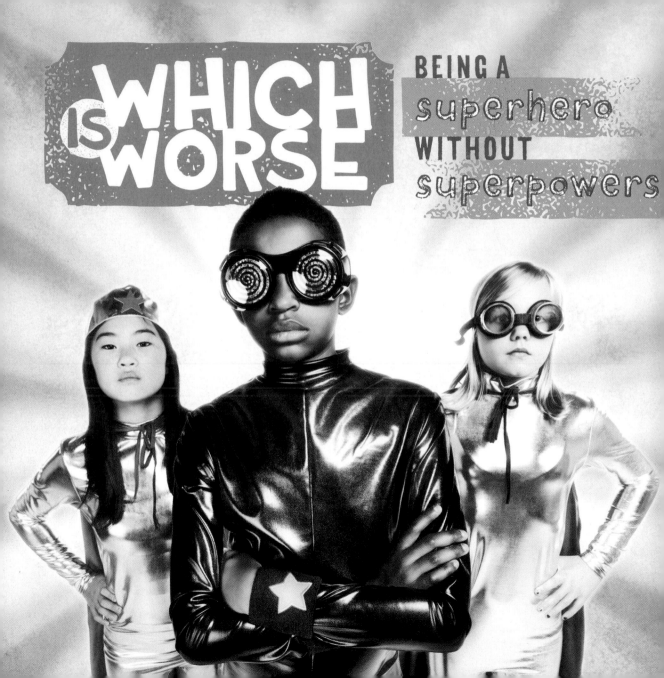

WHICH IS WORSE

(IS)

BEING A **superhero** WITHOUT **superpowers**

◄•OR•►

???

HAVING superpowers YOU CAN never use?

WHICH IS WORSE

BEING TURNED INTO A CHAIR

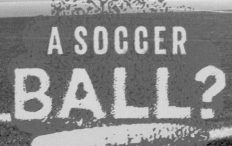

OR

A SOCCER
BALL?

WHICH IS WORSE

NEVER-ENDING loud burps

OR

NEVER-ENDING quiet farts?

WHICH IS WORSE

TODAY

27

LIVING THE SAME DAY OVER AND OVER AGAIN

WHICH IS WORSE

BEING stuck inside WITH NO INTERNET

OR **stuck outside DURING A HEAT WAVE?**

IS WHICH WORSE

NOT BEING ABLE
TO ESCAPE A
**LOCKED
ROOM**

BEING **OR** **TRAPPED OUTSIDE**

YOUR OWN HOUSE?

WHICH IS WORSE

WHICH IS WORSE

TRYING TO STAY AWAKE DURING AN ETERNAL NIGHTTIME

OR

TRYING TO SLEEP DURING AN ETERNAL DAYTIME?

WHICH IS WORSE

A DOG DROOLING RIGHT IN YOUR MOUTH

OR

A CAT THROWING UP A HAIRBALL ON YOUR HEAD?

???

WHICH IS WORSE

HAVING TWO belly buttons

OR → no belly button? ???

WHICH IS WORSE

GETTING LOST IN THE RAIN FOREST

WHICH IS WORSE

HAVING ALLERGIES YEAR-ROUND

◀OR▶ A MONTH-LONG **NOSEBLEED** EVERY YEAR?

???

WHICH IS WORSE

TRYING TO OUTRUN A hungry lion

OR

OUTSWIM A bloodthirsty shark?

WHICH IS WORSE

TELLING SOMEONE YOUR best friend's secret

OR

YOUR best friend TELLING SOMEONE YOUR secret?

???

WHICH IS WORSE

being tickled for an hour **OR** being itchy for an hour?

SMELLING SOMETHING TERRIBLE THAT NOBODY ELSE NOTICES ← OR → NOT BEING ABLE TO TELL WHEN YOU SMELL TERRIBLE?

WHICH IS WORSE

TRAVELING TO THE PAST BUT NOT BEING ABLE TO CHANGE ANYTHING

OR

OR TRAVELING TO THE FUTURE BUT NOT REMEMBERING WHAT YOU SEE?

WHICH IS WORSE

NOT BEING ABLE
TO EAT ANYTHING
SWEET
FOR THE REST OF
YOUR LIFE

OR

NOT BEING ABLE TO EAT ANYTHING SALTY?

???

WHICH IS WORSE

losing YOUR phone

◄OR►

losing YOUR wallet?

???

WHICH IS WORSE

LIVING IN A WORLD WITHOUT TREES

A WORLD **OR** WITHOUT STARS?

WHICH IS WORSE

BEING TRAPPED IN A ROOM FULL OF

POSSESSED PUPPETS

OR

AN ATTIC INHABITED BY AN
EVIL CLOWN?

WHICH IS WORSE

being SHIPWRECKED in the Bermuda Triangle

OR

CRASH-LANDING
in the
Grand Canyon?

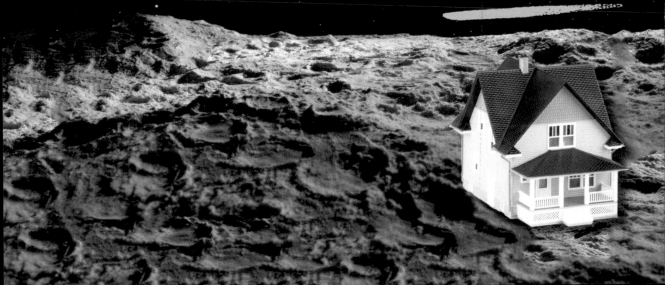

WHICH IS WORSE

HAVING TO FLEE Earth

OR

STAYING
BEHIND
TO LIVE IN A
dystopian
world?

??

WHICH IS WORSE

WASHING A SINK FULL OF *dirty dishes* WITH YOUR tongue

OR CLEANING THE *toilet* WITH YOUR **bare hands?** ???

WHICH IS WORSE

cockroaches
**CRAWLING
ALL OVER
YOUR KITCHEN**

WHICH IS WORSE

LIVING THROUGH A
NUCLEAR
WINTER

OR

???

A CLIMATE CHANGE-INDUCED

TIDAL WAVE?

WHICH IS WORSE

GETTING A bee IN YOUR ear

WHICH IS WORSE

DISCOVERING A **THUMB** ← IN YOUR MAC AND CHEESE

A **TOE** **OR** IN YOUR ROOT BEER FLOAT? **???**

WHICH IS WORSE

having toe fungus OR tongue warts?

WHICH IS WORSE

DOING A HANDSTAND FOR AN HOUR ← OR → BALANCING ON ONE LEG FOR AN HOUR?

WHICH IS WORSE

EXPANDING UNTIL YOU'RE THE SIZE OF A → *house*

OR

SHRINKING DOWN TO THE SIZE OF AN *ant?*

WHICH IS WORSE

GETTING A SPLINTER IN YOUR EYE

OR

A
PAPER CUT
IN YOUR
EYE?

???

WHICH IS WORSE

BEING ETERNALLY *thirsty*  OR ETERNALLY *hungry?*

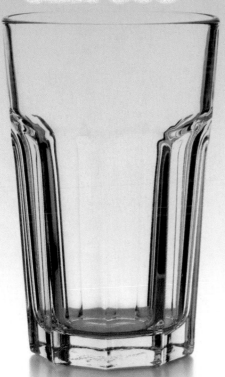

shivering
ALL THE TIME

OR

sweating
**ALL THE
TIME?**

OR

NEVER BEING ABLE TO LEAVE YOUR

HOUSE?

WHICH IS WORSE

BLOODY cupcakes

◀ OR ▶

HAIRY donuts?

???

WHICH IS WORSE

NOT BEING ABLE TO SHOWER FOR A WEEK

OR

WEARING THE SAME UNDERWEAR FOR A WEEK?

WHICH IS WORSE

LISTENING TO FINGERNAILS ON A CHALKBOARD FOR A MINUTE

OR

A FLOCK OF **SCREECHING** BIRDS FOR AN **HOUR?**

WHICH IS WORSE

breathing toxic smog

◄ **OR** ►

drinking **sulfuric water?**

???

WHICH IS WORSE

BREAKING BOTH arms

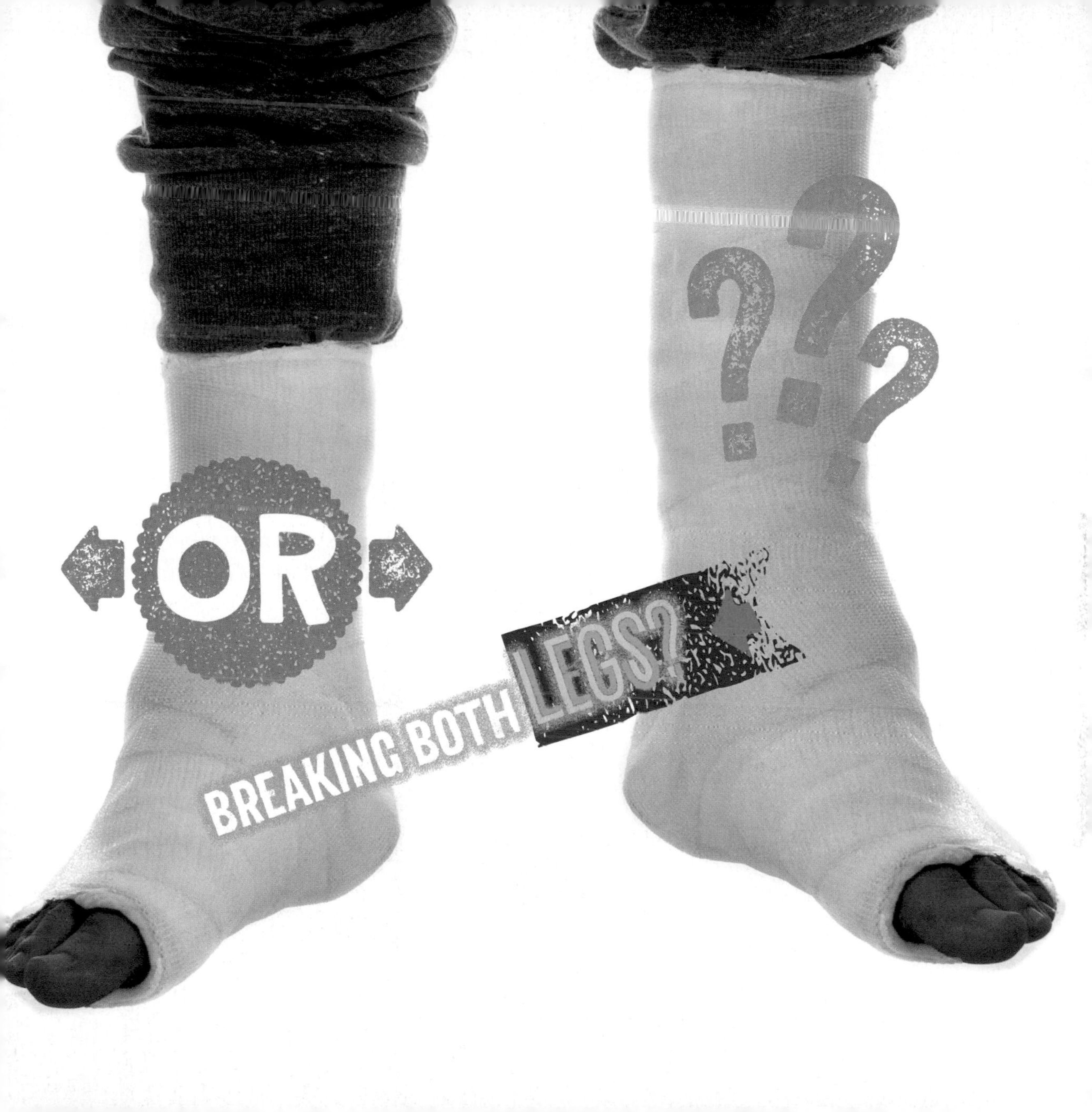
OR
BREAKING BOTH LEGS?

WHICH IS WORSE

HAVING TO MOVE A POUND OF **SAND** WITH ONLY A PAIR OF **TWEEZERS**

OR

A GALLON OF *water* WITH ONLY AN *eyedropper*?

WHICH IS WORSE

EATING month-old PIZZA OR A curdled MILKSHAKE?

WHICH IS WORSE

falling down a flight of STAIRS

◀ OR ▶

OUT OF A TREE?

? ? ?

WHICH IS WORSE

BEING THE ONLY ONE IN YOUR FAMILY WITHOUT SUPERPOWERS

OR

FINDING OUT EVERYONE
IN YOUR FAMILY IS AN
ALIEN?

WHICH IS WORSE

EVERYONE *looking* AT YOU ALL THE TIME

OR

EVERYONE *ignoring* YOU ALL THE TIME?

???

WHICH IS WORSE

GETTING swept UP BY A dust storm

OR

A

tsunami?

???

WHICH IS WORSE

only being able to eat **BABY FOOD FOR LIFE**

OR FOOD *that has gone* BAD?

WHICH IS WORSE

GETTING TRAPPED IN A HIBERNATING BEAR'S DEN

OR

FALLING INTO A
HORNET'S
NEST?

??

WHICH IS WORSE

TRYING TO

ESCAPE A

BURNING

BUILDING

WHICH IS WORSE

WEARING SOGGY SOCKS **OR** moist underwear?

WHICH IS WORSE

SEAWATER SODA ◄ OR ► SEAWEED SALSA?

WHICH IS WORSE

LISTENING TO
NONSTOP
**AIR
HORN**
BLASTS

OR CONSTANT RINGING IN YOUR EARS?

WHICH IS WORSE

getting a SUNBURN all over your BODY

OR

RINGWORM all over your FACE?

WHICH IS WORSE

POOP-SCOOPING

FOR **ONE**

elephant

WHICH IS WORSE
GARLIC *face cream*

WHICH IS WORSE

CLEANING A TOILET WITH YOUR **TOOTHBRUSH**

WHICH IS WORSE

TRYING TO SURVIVE A NIGHT IN A CREEPY OLD MENTAL HOSPITAL

OR

TRYING TO SURVIVE A BATTLE AGAINST A

MEDIEVAL KNIGHT?

WHICH IS WORSE

being brainwashed ‹OR› losing your soul?

YOUR PHONE RUNNING OUT OF BATTERY

OR

OUT OF MEMORY?

Cannot Take Photo
There is not enough available storage to take a photo. You can manage your storage in Settings.

Done   Settings

WHICH IS WORSE

BEING HAUNTED BY A POLTERGEIST

OR **STALKED BY ZOMBIES?**

???

WHICH IS WORSE

Do Not Damage This Ticket

State Lottery

3 22 29

WINNING THE LOTTERY BUT HAVING THE TICKET STOLEN

OR

DAMAGING THE WINNING TICKET BEFORE YOU CAN COLLECT YOUR PRIZE?

Do Not Damage This Ticket

State Lottery

13 22 29 34

???

WHICH IS WORSE

GETTING TRAMPLED BY A WOOLLY MAMMOTH

WHICH IS WORSE

DISCOVERING THAT SOMEONE MADE A CLONE OF YOU

CLONE-1234567890

←**OR**→ → FINDING OUT THAT YOU'RE A **CLONE** OF **SOMEONE** ELSE? ←

CLONE-1234567890

WHICH IS WORSE

finding **LEECHES** stuck all over your body

OR

A RATTLESNAKE coiled on your chest?

???

WHICH IS WORSE

HAVING TO CRASH-LAND A PLANE

OR DRIVE A RUNAWAY TRAIN?

WHICH IS WORSE

TRYING TO WALK OVER thin ice

*OR THROUGH QUICKSAND???

WHICH IS WORSE

being lost in a never-ending **LABYRINTH**

OR *lost at SEA?* **???**

WHICH IS WORSE

GETTING **HIT** BY A **METEORITE**

WHICH IS WORSE — not being able to sleep **OR** not being able to wake up?

COMPETING IN A **TRIATHLON** WITHOUT TRAINING

OR

TAKING A **FINAL EXAM** WITHOUT STUDYING?

WHICH IS WORSE

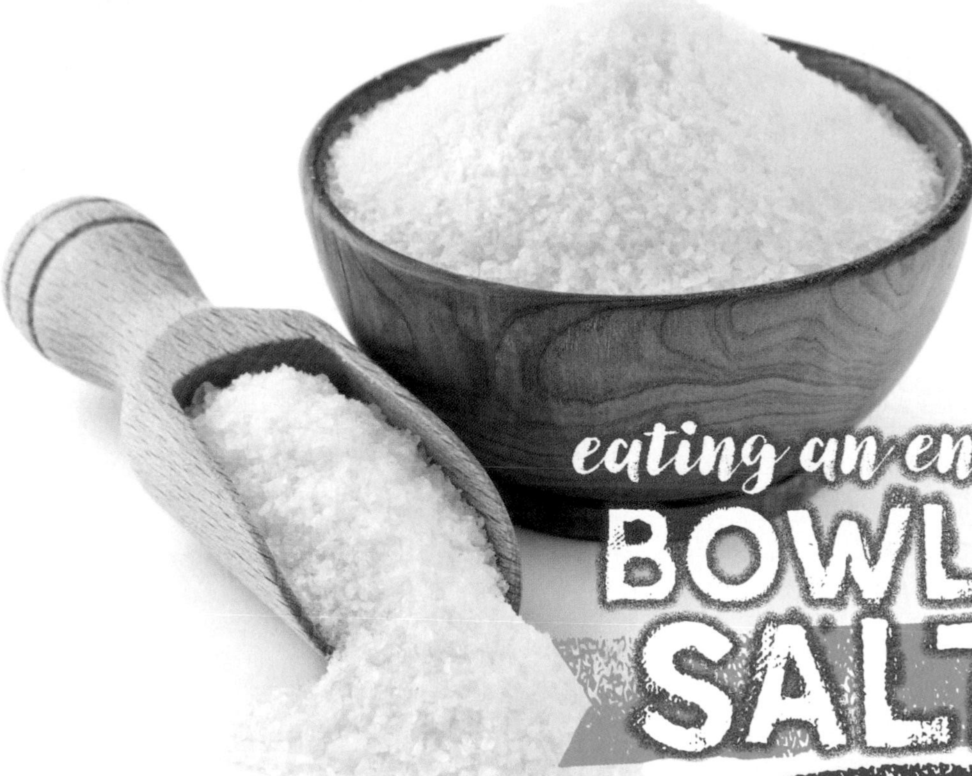

eating an entire
BOWL of SALT

OR *an entire* **BOWL** *of* **PEPPER?**

???

WHICH IS WORSE

being scorched by DRAGON fire

OR impaled by a **UNICORN** horn? ???

WHICH IS WORSE

GROWING
SIX-INCH-LONG
NOSE
HAIR

OR SIX-INCH-LONG **EAR** HAIR?

???

WHICH IS WORSE

SWALLOWING A MOUTHFUL OF spicy WASABI

OR ← → A MOUTHFUL of **soap?**

???

WHICH IS WORSE

USING **mustard** FOR TOOTHPASTE

‹ **OR** ›

vinegar FOR MOUTHWASH

???